Baseball Memories

by Kelly Ann Murphy

HOUGHTON MIFFLIN HARCOURT
School Publishers

Copyright © by Houghton Mifflin Harcourt Publishing Company

All rights reserved. No part of this work may be reproduced or transmitted in any form or by any means, electronic or mechanical, including photocopying or recording, or by any information storage and retrieval system, without the prior written permission of the copyright owner unless such copying is expressly permitted by federal copyright law. Requests for permission to make copies of any part of the work should be addressed to Houghton Mifflin Harcourt School Publishers, Attn: Permissions, 6277 Sea Harbor Drive, Orlando, Florida 32887-6777.

Printed in China

ISBN-10: 0-547-25308-7
ISBN-13: 978-0-547-25308-4

11 12 13 14 0940 19 18 17 16
4500569761

If you have received these materials as examination copies free of charge, Houghton Mifflin Harcourt School Publishers retains title to the materials and they may not be resold. Resale of examination copies is strictly prohibited.

Possession of this publication in print format does not entitle users to convert this publication, or any portion of it, into electronic format.

Contents

A New Town

The photograph of Corey's favorite Chicago baseball team hung next to his bedroom window. A photograph of a man in a baseball uniform hung nearby. The man's brown eyes and brown hair resembled Corey's.

Corey looked out his window at the land. He had lived in this small town in Texas for nearly two months. Corey remembered how large the flat, open space appeared to be when he first arrived. The sweeping views of the new town seemed to go on and on. Every day on his walks to the horse ranch, Corey enjoyed looking at the land and the sky.

Corey's favorite part of living in the new town was working at the Suarez horse ranch. At first, Corey felt nervous around such large animals. Back in Illinois, he had spent time with dogs and cats, but not with large animals. Feeding the horses and taking care of them turned out to be a lot of fun. Corey's friends back in Chicago liked Corey's stories about the horse ranch. They wanted to visit Texas and help with the horses, too. But Corey had a lot to learn before his friends visited!

"Corey, I've got your favorite meal ready! I made peanut butter and jelly sandwiches with carrots," Corey's mother said to him.

"I'll be right there, Mom," Corey said. If Corey were back in Chicago, typically he would be on his way to a baseball game later that day. Corey's entire family loved the game of baseball. Corey's father and mother took Corey to professional baseball games at least a few times every summer.

But this summer was different. No professional baseball teams played in this new town. Luckily, the horse ranch was within walking distance of where Corey lived. Corey had always liked caring for animals. So Corey had decided to help at the ranch to earn money. He learned something new every day.

Corey ate his lunch. He hugged and kissed his mother. Then he put on a baseball hat and headed to the horse ranch.

The bright blue sky and very hot sun sometimes seemed brutal to Corey. Chicago weather could be warm. But Texas heat was humid, which means wet. Sometimes Corey didn't think that he would ever be able to stop sweating. In Chicago, Corey could cool off by swimming in Lake Michigan. There were no lakes near where Corey lived now, although one boy who lived on Corey's street had a swimming pool and sometimes invited him over to swim. Somehow, swimming in a pool wasn't the same as swimming in Lake Michigan.

Corey gazed up at the bright sunshine and the clear sky. He thought, *I love this new place. But I miss my friends in Chicago. I miss the lake. And I miss my baseball teams!*

Corey's new home is in horse ranching country.

5

The Horse Ranch

"Hey, Corey! Hurry up! I want to feed the horses, and I need your help!" Corey's friend, Luisa, called from the distance. Luisa had lived in Texas all her life. Her family owned the horse ranch. Luisa had explained to Corey how to brush and care for the animals. The horses seemed so comfortable when Luisa handled them. Corey had liked her instantly.

Corey greeted Luisa and told her how hot he felt. He wondered how people stayed cool in Texas. Luisa replied, "Well, I guess we try not to think about the heat too much. Besides, when I am around the horses, I don't think about anything else. I just take care of them and before I know it, the day is over. Do you know what I mean?"

Corey smiled. "Yes, I think I do. So I guess we should stop talking and start working, right?"

Corey followed Luisa into the stable.

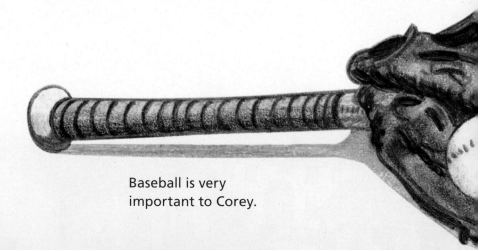

Baseball is very
important to Corey.

The horses were happy to see Luisa and Corey and made friendly snorting sounds. Some of the horses were females, or mares. Corey grabbed some oats from hanging buckets and refilled each feeding bin. As he did so, his cell phone beeped. Corey looked down and he saw that a friend from Chicago had just sent him a text message. Corey's favorite baseball team had just won an important game! His friend had been there to watch it. His team's opponents had played well. But Corey's team had played better.

Luisa noticed that Corey seemed sad all of the sudden. "Hey, Corey, what's the matter? Wait, I know—that baseball team that you like played today, right? Did they lose?"

"No, Luisa. They won," Corey told her.

Luisa looked at him, smiling. "Well, that's great news! So why do you look so sad?"

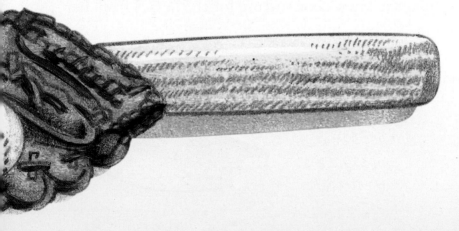

Corey thought for a moment. Then he said, "I miss my friends in Chicago, Luisa. Even though I love it here . . . I'm having a hard time. The gorgeous landscape and helping you with the horses are wonderful. But I miss going to baseball games with my dad and my friends. I miss playing on my old baseball team."

"It takes a lot of courage to admit that you are sad, Corey. I hope you are never too embarrassed to tell me how you feel," said Luisa.

Corey smiled and shook his head. "I think it's harder because this place is so different from Chicago. Sometimes that's what I like about being here. But sometimes that's what makes it hard. I'm really glad we are friends. It helps to talk to you, Luisa."

A sudden noise stirred the horses. They had heard Mr. Suarez enter the stable. Mr. Suarez owned the ranch. He was Luisa's uncle, and he laughed all the time. He treated the horses as if they were his children. Luisa had learned everything she knew about caring for the horses from her uncle.

"It is nice to see you both, Luisa and Corey," Mr. Suarez said. He looked at some charts hanging on the wall. "I need to get three of the mares out for exercise today. They haven't been out for a few days. I'll need you both to help me with that. Horses need a lot of exercise to stay healthy. Would you both like to go riding with me this evening?"

The thought of riding later made Corey feel happy. "Sure, Mr. Suarez, that would be really fun. I might need some advice on how to ride, though. I'm still learning. But do you think it will be too hot to take the horses out?"

Mr. Suarez and Luisa smiled at each other. Then Luisa said, "You know, Corey, we try not to talk about the heat so much, but we *do* have ways to adapt to it! I'll show you one simple trick when we go out later."

Each horse stall in the stable contained a water bucket. Mr. Suarez looked inside one. "It might be hot enough today to put ice into the water buckets. The ice will melt throughout the day and keep the water cool for the horses. We can also leave the doors open at each end of the barn so that, hopefully, a breeze will blow through to cool the horses."

After Luisa and Corey finished feeding the horses, they spent some time filling the buckets with ice from the freezer in the house. They poured cool water over the ice in each bucket, and then they put the buckets back in each stall.

A Horse Ride

Later that day, Corey returned to the horse ranch. Luisa and Mr. Suarez were preparing the three horses for the ride. Mr. Suarez put a saddle on each horse. Luisa tightened the bridles and reins of each horse. It was obvious how much they enjoyed taking care of the horses.

Corey approached the horses carefully. He put his hand on one mare's shoulder, as Luisa had taught him to do. "It looks like you are learning quickly, Corey!" Mr. Suarez said. "Do you want to help me tighten the saddles?"

As Corey and Mr. Suarez finished getting the horses ready, Luisa ran back to the house. A few minutes later, she returned. Luisa carried a few frozen cloths. "Remember you were worried about staying cool, Corey? Well, here's some advice for you. Place a few of these cloths beneath your helmet before riding. They will keep you cool."

The horse ranch is a peaceful place.

The frozen cloths reminded Corey of his old baseball team. He explained to Luisa and Mr. Suarez how his baseball teammates would do the same thing. Players could place their cloths in a team cooler filled with ice. This preliminary activity was important on a hot day. Later, the players could keep cool by wrapping the cloths around their necks.

Mr. Suarez smiled. "Corey, I used to do the same thing when I played baseball!"

This news surprised Corey. He had not known that Mr. Suarez played baseball.

The three of them started riding toward the horse path. Mr. Suarez told stories about baseball games that had been played in the local community. Corey learned that many of the games were played near the path they were riding along.

"I don't understand, Mr. Suarez," Corey said. "I've been here all summer. But I haven't seen any baseball fields or any kids playing baseball. What happened to the baseball fields near your house?"

Mr. Suarez told Corey and Luisa that the local community had changed. Many families had left their ranches. They had moved to big cities. "We don't have enough families living here any more to form baseball leagues. It's been a long time since we have had a baseball game in town," Mr. Suarez explained. "I miss my old friends. But I would never leave my ranch and my horses." He patted his mare and smiled. "It's supposedly better in the big city. I like the city, but I like my ranch even better."

Riding is fun for horses and for people.

Home at Last

The next day, Corey was awake before his parents. Mr. Suarez's stories the night before had given him an idea. He sat at the computer desk in his parents' office. A Web page about local baseball history showed old team photographs.

Corey's parents walked into the office. He told his parents about the baseball stories Mr. Suarez had shared. Corey showed his parents the Web page. "Look, I found a photograph of Mr. Suarez's old baseball team! Supposedly, he was their star pitcher. I am going to print a copy of this photo, put it in a frame, and give it to him," Corey said.

Corey's mother said that was a very nice idea. She got a frame from the basement that Corey could use.

Later that day, Corey went to the Suarez horse ranch. He carried the framed photograph in one hand, and two baseball gloves and a baseball in the other hand.

Luisa and Mr. Suarez were spreading hay around the pasture. They looked up and greeted Corey. Corey presented Mr. Suarez with the framed photograph. "I wanted to give you something to show you how much I enjoyed listening to your stories last night, Mr. Suarez," Corey explained while feeling a little bit embarrassed.

Mr. Suarez smiled. "This is really special, Corey. I haven't seen this photo in a long time. Thank you for doing this. Hey, what else did you bring with you?"

Luisa laughed and pointed at the baseball gloves. "I think Corey is officially going to become the first horse rancher who also plays baseball!"

They all laughed. Corey smiled at Luisa, tossing the baseball into the air. "Well, that will make *two* of us! Come on, let's play a quick game of catch before we feed the horses."

Responding

✔ **TARGET SKILL** **Theme** What is the theme of this story? Think of three related ideas that contribute to the theme. Copy and complete the graphic organizer below.

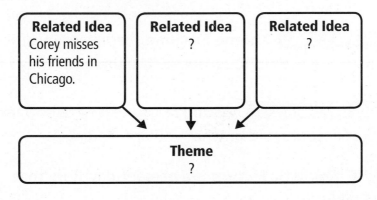

Related Idea
Corey misses his friends in Chicago.

Related Idea
?

Related Idea
?

Theme
?

Write About It

Text to Self Corey misses his old home, but he also finds his new home interesting. Have you ever had different emotions about something in your life? Write a paragraph describing something you have had both good and bad feelings about.

brutal	opponents
embarrassed	preliminary
gorgeous	sweeping
obvious	supposedly
officially	typically

✔ **TARGET SKILL** **Theme** Examine characters' qualities, motives, and actions to recognize the theme of the story.

✔ **TARGET STRATEGY** **Visualize** Use text details to form pictures in your mind of what you are reading.

GENRE **Realistic Fiction** is a present-day story that could take place in real life.